Wipe-clean
Times Tables

Illustrated by Elisa Paganelli

Written by Holly Bathie
Designed by Maddison Warnes

Zeb

Wolfy

There are answers,
and secret notes
for grown-ups at
the back of the book.

Edited by Jessica Greenwell
Series Editor: Felicity Brooks

Pat

Times tables reminder

Each of these bugs has 3 spots. Pat has written in the boxes how many bugs are on each leaf. Use the 3 times table to find the total number of spots on each leaf without counting.

These pages will help you to remember the 3, 4, 6 and 8 times tables.

Pat

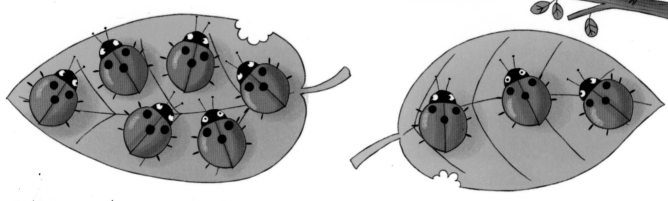

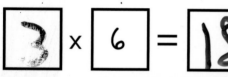

$3 \times 6 = 18$

$3 \times 3 = 9$

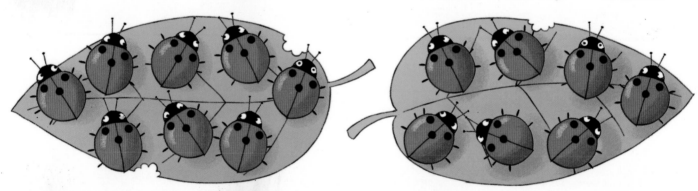

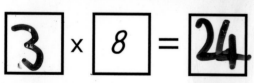

$3 \times 8 = 24$

$3 \times 7 = 21$

Wipe the page clean.

Check you can remember the 6 times table by doubling the number of spots on each bug. (You could draw more spots to help you, so that they each have 6.) Then complete the new calculations.

Bruce

Help Gloria with her calculations to see if you can remember the 4 times table.

Every butterfly has 4 spots. Use the 4 times table to find the total number of spots in each group without counting.

I've written the number of butterflies in each group for you.

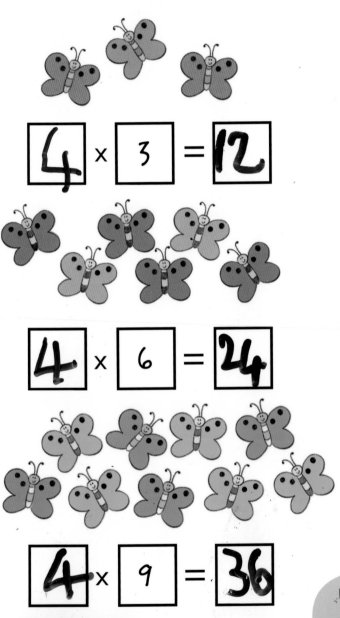

$4 \times 3 = 12$

$4 \times 6 = 24$

$4 \times 9 = 36$

$4 \times 10 = 40$

$4 \times 8 = 32$

Butterflies are symmetrical. That means the patterns on their wings are mirror images of each other.

Wipe the page clean.

Check you can remember the 8 times table by doubling the number of spots on each butterfly. (You could draw more spots to help you, so that they each have 8.) Complete the new calculations.

Groups of 7

Ping is fishing at an ice hole and wants to work out how many fish there are in the water. Draw a ring around 7 fish, then draw a ring around another group of 7. Keep going until all the fish are in groups of 7.

Plenty of fish today!

Ping

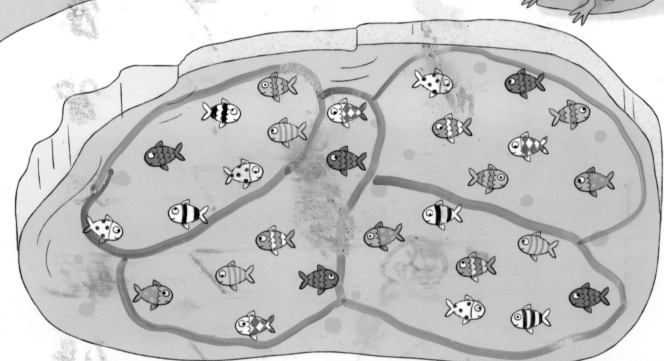

Count how many groups you have made, then complete this calculation.

Do you already know these calculations from other times tables?

 x 7 = 28

If there were double the number of groups, how many fish would there be? Complete this calculation to find out.

8 x 7 = 56

The 7 times table

Can you help the penguins complete this times table? You may know some of the calculations from other tables.

I know the 2, 5 and 10 times tables, so I can fill in those answers.

I know the 3, 4, 6 and 8 times tables, so I can fill those in.

Now we just need to add or subtract 7 to fill in any gaps in the table.

You could use the number line at the bottom of the page to help you.

1	× 7	=	7
2	× 7	=	14
3	× 7	=	21
4	× 7	=	28
5	× 7	=	35
6	× 7	=	42
7	× 7	=	49
8	× 7	=	56
9	× 7	=	63
10	× 7	=	70

Subtract 7 ↑

Add 7 ↓

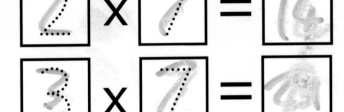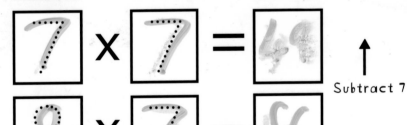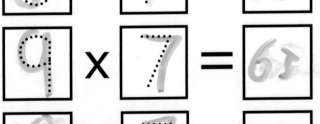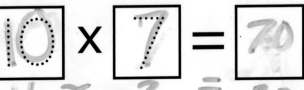

42   49   56   63   70

Groups of 9

Bruce is busy in the sweetshop putting out all the sweets in trays of 9. Help the mice complete the labels for him.

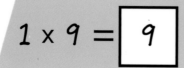

I've got 1 row of 9 lemon drops.

$1 \times 9 = \boxed{9}$

$2 \times 9 = \boxed{18}$

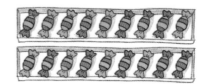

Phew! Lots to count.

$3 \times 9 = \boxed{27}$

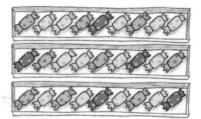

These sweets aren't ready yet. Can we still finish the label?

Ummmm...

$4 \times 9 = \boxed{36}$

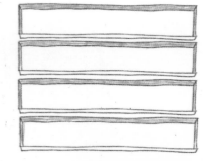

Yes, we can do it. The answer will be 9 more than the last label.

So let's count in 9s: 9, 18, 27...

I wonder if there's an easier way...

Bruce knows the 10 times table and thinks he could help the mice.

Pin, let's put out **4** more sweets – 1 more for each tray. Then we'll have 4 trays of 10 instead. That would be easier.

4 lots of 10 is **40**.

But there's no room for another sweet on each tray, Bruce.

Ok, **I'll** take these **4** sweets away then. 40 take away **4** is 36.

Oh, that must be the answer! 4 lots of 9 is 36.

Pin

Hooray!

Can you complete the next label, using the 10 times table to help you? (The numbers in the blue boxes will be the same.)

$5 \times 10 \ = \ \boxed{50}$

$\boxed{5} - 5 = \boxed{0}$

$5 \times 9 = \boxed{45}$

Write another 9 times table calculation here. (You could use the 10 times table to help you.)

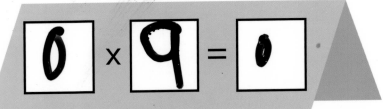

$\boxed{0} \times \boxed{9} = \boxed{0}$

Wipe your calculation clean.

When you've wiped this calculation clean, you could try writing some more 9 times table calculations. Wipe the calculation clean after each one.

Groups of 11

The mice are making bunting for the fair and want to put 11 paper flags on each string. They have put 10 on each string so far. Complete their 10 times table calculations.

Hold tight!

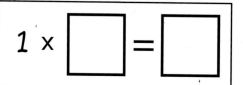

$$1 \times \boxed{} = \boxed{}$$

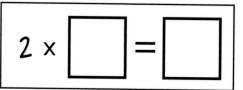

$$2 \times \boxed{} = \boxed{}$$

$$3 \times \boxed{} = \boxed{}$$

Wipe all the boxes clean.

When you have wiped all the boxes clean, draw 1 more flag on each string for the mice and complete the 11 times table calculations.

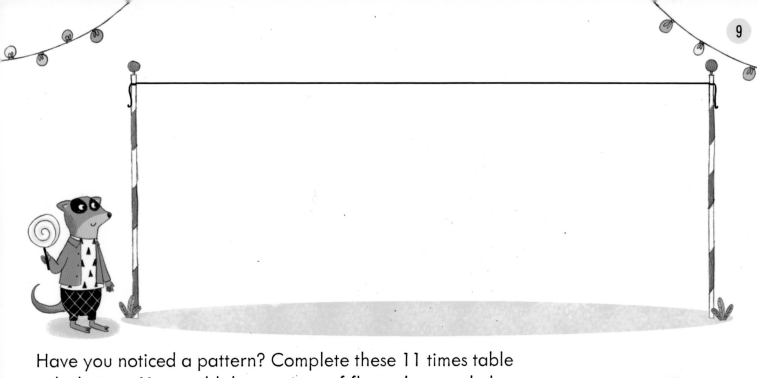

Have you noticed a pattern? Complete these 11 times table calculations. You could draw strings of flags above to help you.

 x **=**

 x **=**

Write another 11 times table calculation below.

 x **=**

Wipe your calculation clean.

Try writing as many 11 times table calculations as you can. Wipe your calculation clean after each one.

If you want to try the 12 times table, wipe all the boxes clean and write some more calculations using 12.

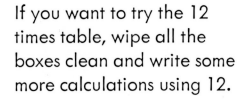

Pop!

Ooops!

You could draw another flag on each string to help you complete the 12 times table calculations.

The 9 and 11 times tables

Hop and Zeb are spotting patterns in this number grid. Hop has circled the first few numbers in the 9 times table. Can you circle the rest?

I've counted 9 three times to get to 27. 3 lots of 9 is 27.

Draw a triangle around each of the numbers in the 11 times table for me, please.

1	2	3	4	5	6	7	8	9	10
11	12	13	14	15	16	17	18	19	20
21	22	23	24	25	26	27	28	29	30
31	32	33	34	35	36	37	38	39	40
41	42	43	44	45	46	47	48	49	50
51	52	53	54	55	56	57	58	59	60
61	62	63	64	65	66	67	68	69	70
71	72	73	74	75	76	77	78	79	80
81	82	83	84	85	86	87	88	89	90
91	92	93	94	95	96	97	98	99	100
101	102	103	104	105	106	107	108	109	110

Zeb

Which number is in both the 9 times table and the 11 times table? Write it in this box.

Help Kat complete these times tables.

The 9 times table

1	x	9	=	
2	x	9	=	
3	x	9	=	
4	x	9	=	
5	x	9	=	
6	x	9	=	
7	x	9	=	
8	x	9	=	
9	x	9	=	
10	x	9	=	

The 11 times table

1	x	11	=	
2	x	11	=	
3	x	11	=	
4	x	11	=	
5	x	11	=	
6	x	11	=	
7	x	11	=	
8	x	11	=	
9	x	11	=	
10	x	11	=	

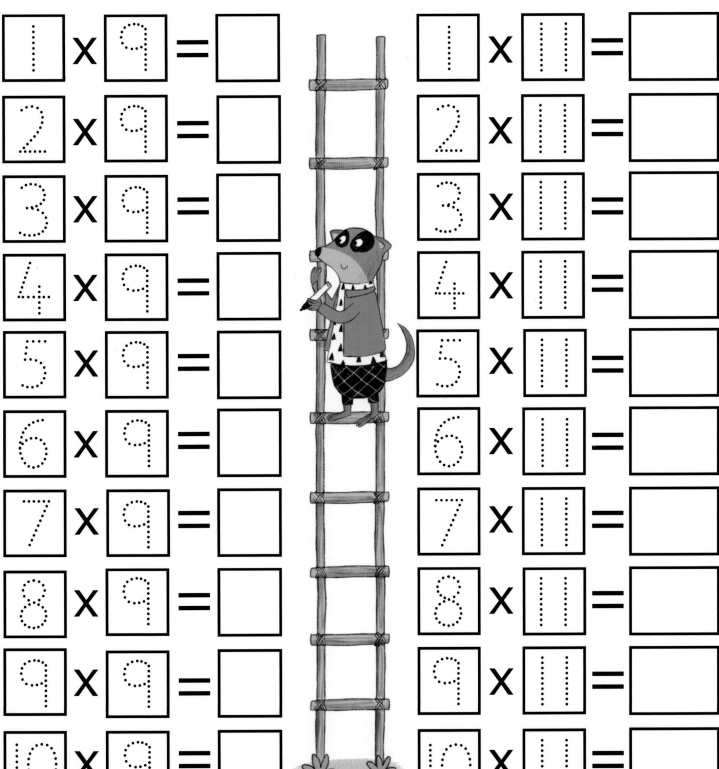

Can you see any patterns?

No, it's too dark down here!

Word problems for 9 and 11

Wolfy, Bruce and Hop are growing flowers in the garden. Write a multiplying calculation to answer each animal's question.

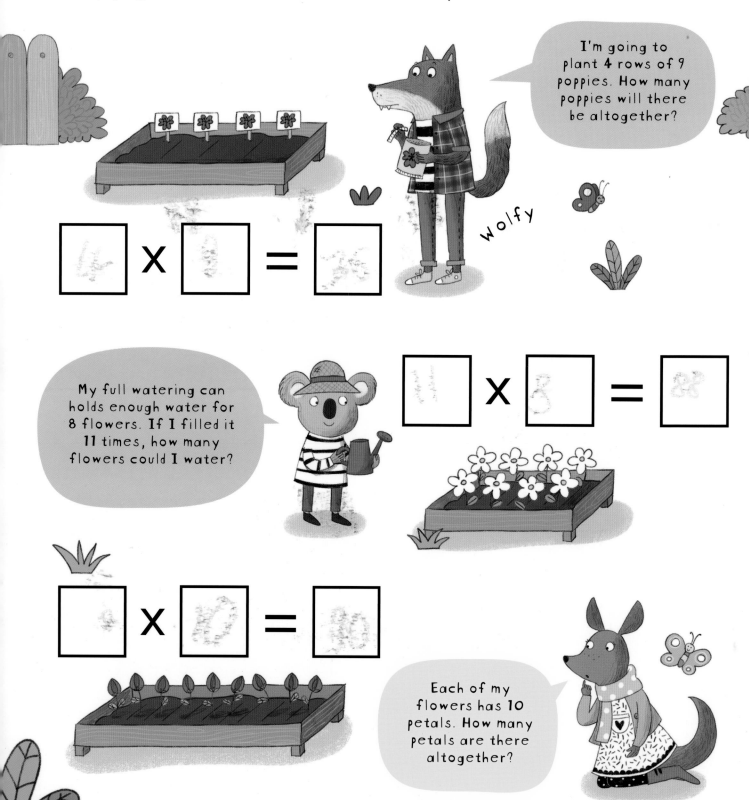

I'm going to plant 4 rows of 9 poppies. How many poppies will there be altogether?

Wolfy

My full watering can holds enough water for 8 flowers. If I filled it 11 times, how many flowers could I water?

Each of my flowers has 10 petals. How many petals are there altogether?

9   18   27   36   45   54   63   72   81   90

Pin, Gloria and Kat are growing vegetables.
Write a multiplying calculation to answer
each animal's question.

Each pea pod has 11 peas inside. How many peas are there altogether?

☐ X ☐ = ☐

I have sown 9 carrot seeds in each row. How many seeds have I sown altogether?

☐ X ☐ = ☐

How many peppers will there be if 9 grow on each plant?

☐ X ☐ = ☐

(11) (22) (33) (44) (55) (66) (77) (88) (99) (110)

The 12 times table

Count along the number grid in 12s and draw a circle around each number in the 12 times table.

The 12 times table goes past 100!

Add more numbers to the bottom part of the grid to continue the pattern up to 12 lots of 12.

1	2	3	4	5	6	7	8	9	10
11	12	13	14	15	16	17	18	19	20
21	22	23	24	25	26	27	28	29	30
31	32	33	34	35	36	37	38	39	40
41	42	43	44	45	46	47	48	49	50
51	52	53	54	55	56	57	58	59	60
61	62	63	64	65	66	67	68	69	70
71	72	73	74	75	76	77	78	79	80
81	82	83	84	85	86	87	88	89	90
91	92	93	94	95	96	97	98	99	100

12   24   36   48   60   72

Now that you have finished the grid, complete the 12 times table.

To check your answers, remember 12 is double 6, so you can double all the numbers in the 6 times table to get the 12 times table.

1 x 6 = 6
2 x 6 = 12
3 x 6 = 18
4 x 6 = 24
5 x 6 = 30
6 x 6 = 36
7 x 6 = 42
8 x 6 = 48
9 x 6 = 54
10 x 6 = 60

Hurry up, Bruce!

Check the answers on page 25 to see if you are right.

1 X 12 =
2 X 12 =
3 X 12 =
4 X 12 =
5 X 12 =
6 X 12 =
7 X 12 =
8 X 12 =
9 X 12 =
10 X 12 =
11 X 12 =
12 X 12 =

84   96   108   120   132   144

Word problems for 7 and 12

The animals are off on holiday. Write a multiplying calculation to answer each of their questions.

☐ × ☐ = ☐

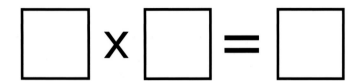

☐ × ☐ = ☐

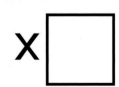

☐ × ☐ = ☐

7   14   21   28   35   42   49   56   63   70

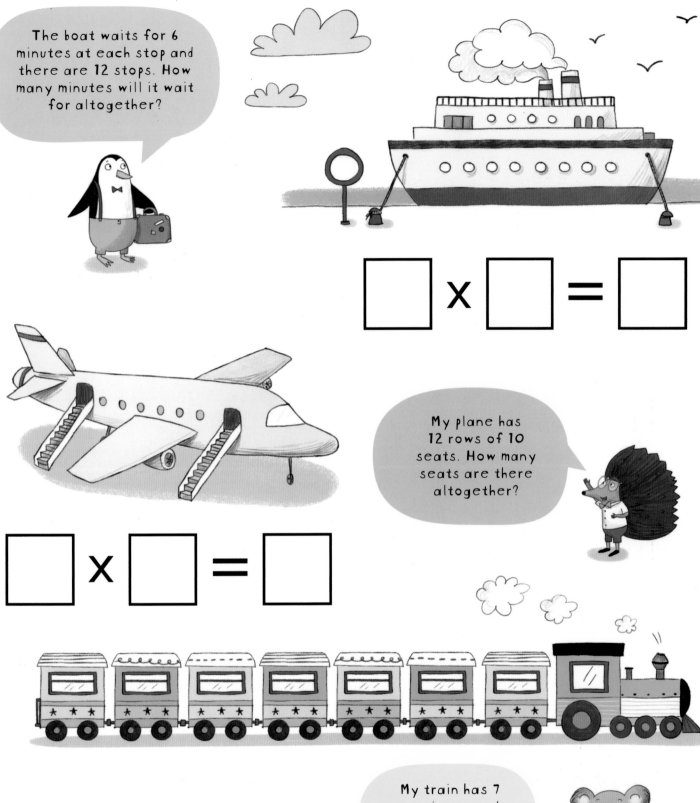

The boat waits for 6 minutes at each stop and there are 12 stops. How many minutes will it wait for altogether?

☐ X ☐ = ☐

☐ X ☐ = ☐

My plane has 12 rows of 10 seats. How many seats are there altogether?

☐ X ☐ = ☐

My train has 7 carriages and each carriage has 7 seats. How many seats are there altogether?

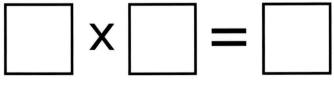

(12) (24) (36) (48) (60) (72) (84) (96) (108) (120)

Multiplication square

This multiplication square lists all the tables vertically, in columns.
The tables are also listed horizontally, in rows.

The 2 times table is down this column.

The 10 times table is down this column.

The 2 times table is along this row, too.

x	1	2	3	4	5	6	7	8	9	10	11	12
1	1	2	3	4	5	6	7	8	9	10	11	12
2	2	4	6	8	10	12	14	16	18	20	22	24
3	3	6	9	12	15	18	21	24	27	30	33	36
4	4	8	12	16	20	24	28	32	36	40	44	48
5	5	10	15	20	25	30	35	40	45	50	55	60
6	6	12	18	24	30	36	42	48	54	60	66	72
7	7	14	21	28	35	42	49	56	63	70	77	84
8	8	16	24	32	40	48	56	64	72	80	88	96
9	9	18	27	36	45	54	63	72	81	90	99	108
10	10	20	30	40	50	60	70	80	90	100	110	120
11	11	22	33	44	55	66	77	88	99	110	121	132
12	12	24	36	48	60	72	84	96	108	120	132	144

Can you find the 10 times table row that matches Pin's 10 times table column? Try finding the matching row for each of the other columns, too.

Choose a number from the yellow row along the top of the square, and a number from the green column down the side, to multiply together. Write them in the boxes below.

To find the answer, run one finger down the column of the yellow number and another finger along the row of the green number. The answer is where your fingers meet. Complete your calculation.

This square is really useful.

Wipe the calculation clean.

When you have wiped your calculation clean, write multiplying calculations for other yellow and green numbers. Wipe the calculation clean after each one.

Draw in the fishing lines to help the animals catch the answers to their calculations. You could use the multiplication square to help you.

9 x 5   9 x 3   7 x 8

27

56

45

Practice for all the times tables

The animals are playing games at the fair. Work out their scores at each stall. You could use this blank calculation to help you. Wipe it clean after each score.

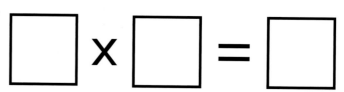

Draw a star next to the animal who has the highest score at the fair.

Times tables quiz

Find out how much you can remember about the 7, 9, 11 and
12 times tables by doing this quiz. Answers on page 24.

A. Can you help the animals with this matching game?
Draw a loopy line to match each times table question
to its correct answer in one of the circles.

⬤ 77

⬤ 108

⬤ 72

| 7 | x | 11 |

⬤ 72

⬤ 108

| 12 | x | 9 |

| 8 | x | 9 |

| 6 | x | 12 |

| 9 | x | 12 |

B. Complete these times tables calculations for Pin and Wolfy.

7 x 6 = ☐ 62

8 x 7 = ☐ 56

8 x 12 = ☐ 96

9 x 11 = ☐ 11

12 x 7 = ☐ 84

7 x 9 = ☐ 63

10 x 11 = ☐ 110

9 x 6 = ☐ 54

7 x 3 = ☐ 21

11 x 12 = ☐ 137

7 x 12 = ☐ 84

12 x 12 = ☐ 144

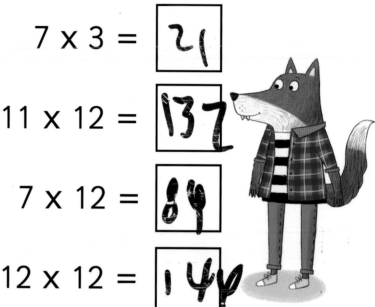

Quiz answers

A.

B.

7 x 6 = 42	10 x 11 = 110
8 x 7 = 56	9 x 6 = 54
8 x 12 = 96	7 x 3 = 21
9 x 11 = 99	11 x 12 = 132
12 x 7 = 84	7 x 12 = 84
7 x 9 = 63	12 x 12 = 144

There are two answer possibilities for 36, 72 and 108. You may have joined them up the other way to the answers shown here.

Score 1 point for each correct answer and write your score in this box: If you want to get a higher score, wipe the pages clean and try again.

21